MW00628645

METABOLIC BOOSTING SMOOTHIES & GOURMET COFFEES

METABOLIC BOOSTING SMOOTHIES & GOURMET COFFEES

Lisa Lynn

Fitness & Metabolic Weight Loss Expert

Wall Street Journal Best Selling Author

Seen on Dr. Oz, Martha Stewart, FOX & Friends, ABC, NBC

Published by LynFit Nutrition

METABOLIC BOOSTING SMOOTHIES & GOURMET COFFEES

Lisa Lynn

Printed in the United States of America

ISBN: 978-0-9908216-4-9

CONTENTS

INTRODUCTION

Welcome to the incredibly delicious and nutritious world of metabolic boosting LynFit smoothies and gourmet coffees.

Over the years, I've collected and tested recipes in my kitchen, consulted with my friends and health experts, brainstormed with my chef friends, and put Martha Stewart to work taste-testing these simple but slimming recipes I'm sharing with you in this guide.

LynFit is best known for its delicious, clean, pure whey protein. It's well-known for its metabolic boosting, fat burning, health-improving abilities. With extreme humility, we say these smoothies, snacks, and desserts will change your life in ways you've never imagined, in addition to improving your health and weight loss.

The only hard part is you must choose which recipe to start with. I suggest starting with a new one each week to spread the enjoyment out through the entire year. You'll enjoy losing weight once you find your favorite smoothies and gourmet coffees.

What makes our whey protein so special that Dr. Oz invited us to tell his viewers about them? They **boost** metabolism!

Most smoothies are designed to deliver a boatload of excess calories and contain three times the amount of sugar that any of us should eat in an entire day. They also STOP fat burning in its tracks, which basically cancels out any health benefits you can get.

LynFit created a purified (lactose-free), clean, premium whey protein that tastes so good you'll question how it can help you lose weight. Like you may have heard me say on the Dr. Oz

Show: Research… inspired by nature, perfected by LynFit Nutrition.

I tracked down the world's best flavorists (literally to Belgium and back) and then began my *must taste so delicious you crave it* tasting, along with Martha Stewart by my side. You'll soon see that these are not only the best shakes for your metabolism, making weight loss faster and easier, but they are also the best for whole-body health.

They will help decrease and control inflammation (so even your aches and pains will feel better), boost healing, lower blood pressure, kill cravings, improve focus and memory, tighten loose skin, and firm and tone muscles, just to name a few. You'll also notice your hair and nails will begin to grow like weeds and become healthier.

WHAT MAKES OUR WHEY PROTEIN DIFFERENT?

LynFit Whey Protein is clean and pure, with no lactose. Nothing but high-grade amino acids that also make it froth and foam, which allows you to make all your favorite gourmet coffees, snacks, and desserts, including ice cream.

The reason this protein powder can be heated is because the grade used is so superior to store-bought protein, meaning even if you lose a little of the protein's value (which can occur when heating protein), you'll still be getting a better quality protein. And you'll know it because you'll see (the scale never lies) and feel the difference.

What could be better than having a protein powder around that's uber-healthy for you, satisfy cravings, and can be used as healthier replacements for your favorite foods?

So, the next time you're craving a guilty pleasure, forget the expensive coffee shops or take-out fare; go with LynFit's guiltless, gourmet-tasting, metabolic boosting protein powder instead. You can shake it, bake it, cook it, drink it, or .... your imagination is the only limit.

It's the perfect way to warm up or cool down and tastes like it came out of the gourmet coffee shop, but without all the fat, sugar, or carbs. It's more filling and will help you avoid overeating or block fat-burning.

My favorite is the Chocolate Truffle and Salted Caramel, not only because it's good for your metabolism, but it's also as delicious as it is nutritious and will help you balance blood sugar levels, which kills cravings and makes losing weight faster and easier.

You must try them mixed together with black coffee; it's a game-changer.

A shake a day keeps the pounds and inflammation away. Drink to health!

Made with LOVE ♡

YOU ARE WHAT YOU DRINK...

Drink metabolically!
#LiveLynFitLean

METABOLIC BOOSTING SMOOTHIES & GOURMET COFFEES

THE METABOLIC CLEAN CAFE

The drinks in the Metabolic Boosting Clean Cafe are specifically designed to boost metabolism, accelerate weight loss and fat burning, and make you look and feel better fast. Not to worry, they are delicious too!

Coffee (black coffee, minus all the unhealthy stuff we add in) can be one of the best things for your metabolism and brain health. What most people don't realize is that all the added sugars, creamers, and unassuming almond and coconut milk may be to blame for your cup's high-calorie count, preventing you from losing weight. Don't take my word for it, test this out for yourself and you'll soon see how much weight you'll lose learning how to drink your coffee in a healthier way.

Don't worry… I've got an even more delicious, metabolic boosting, nutritious way to enjoy the best part of your day. I should warn you though, it's addicting. Luckily, it's one of the best things you can do for your health and saves you time and money.

THINGS YOU NEED TO KNOW

Did you know that adding one tiny packet of sugar or a splash of milk (it doesn't matter whether it's soy, almond, or coconut - this includes Keto oils and products added to coffee) may only contain four grams of sugar? What you might not realize, however, is that these add-in's spike blood sugar levels, putting the brakes on weight loss and turning the weight gain, fat-storing switch to full power on, making it impossible to lose weight or burn off any fat, even if you only have a little.

Not only that, but these add-ins are also bad for your health and have a reputation for weakening growth immune health, which is linked to sarcopenia. Sarcopenia is age-related loss of muscle that slows metabolism, causes osteoporosis, obesity, diabetes, heart disease, and triggers overeating.

A splash of Melt Fat Milk or Frothed Complete Protein Shake goes a long way. If you've been pouring a half cup's worth of the milky stuff, you may be adding more calories than you and preventing your body from burning fat.

If you're using the seemingly healthy milk alternatives (especially the latest craze of Keto kinds of milk, creamers and coffee add-ins), know that these products were developed for bodybuilders who reduced carbs and couldn't get enough calories to build muscle (aka weight gain). Even the plant-based products are packed with added sugars, fats, and unnecessary thickeners, fillers, and emulsifiers. Don't buy into the label claims. The scale will quickly show you, and the scale never lies.

Don't worry; if you're married to adding these diet-wrecking ingredients to your coffee or tea, I've got a healthier, metabolic boosting, and more delicious solution for you that will knock your socks off!

This Metabolic Cafe will show you how using zero-calorie, warm spices such as nutmeg, cloves, and cinnamon — which have been proven to stabilize your blood sugar — along with Metabolic Boosting Complete Protein frothed or made as Melt Fat Milk can help you enjoy your coffee, not just because it's more delicious, but also because you're improving every aspect of your health and making it easier to lose weight and burn off belly fat.

I do suggest buying organic whenever possible and try new spices like Simply Organic Chai Coffee Spice, Awaken Blend Cinnamon, or Pumpkin Spice. Add a tablespoon to your ground coffee or before brewing. These spices are so delicious you'll want to get out of bed in the morning.

POWDERED CREAMERS YOUR PLEASURE?

Powdered, non-dairy or dairy creamers should be called weight gain in a teaspoon because of the unhealthy ingredients they contain, such as anti-aging agents that are also found in detergents that are linked to skin, eye, and respiratory irritations. You'll also find hydrogenated vegetable oil, which adds to the heart-harming saturated fat content, lurking in the ingredient list.

So that "one cup" of coffee every morning might be the reason you're not losing weight and gaining fat around your mid-section at record speed.

Before you throw in the towel and decide that weight loss isn't worth giving up your only pleasure every day, trust me, it's not just the coffee.

I'm going to show you how to make the best-tasting coffee you've ever tried that's so good for your health you should drink it every day. Every time you drink one of these Metabolic Café recipes, you're:

- Boosting metabolism 25%
- Feeding muscle and starving fat
- Saving 380-750 calories
- Saving 50+ grams of sugar
- Virtually eliminating fat grams

LIKE WHIPPED CREAM? WHIP IT GOOD FOR WEIGHT LOSS

If you're like me and a lover of those dessert-like coffees, you're gonna love these metabolic drinks. This guide shows you how to make metabolic, fat-burning whipped cream that's light and airy to top your espresso or latte without the fattening calories or hydrogenated vegetable oil and high fructose corn syrup.

LIKE IT LARGE OR VENTI IN STARBUCKS TALK?

Go for it… because you can :)

Just be careful with getting too much caffeine. The upper daily caffeine limit is 400 milligrams, and you can easily surpass that quota when you buy your coffee away from home.

A venti-sized Blonde Roast packs in a whopping 475 milligrams of the binge-triggering, anxiety-producing stuff. When it comes to weight loss, caffeine is helpful, but not if you take in too much.

Brewing your coffee at home allows you to control the amount of caffeine you take in daily and balance it with the energizing vitamins and minerals in LynFit Accelerator Advanced, LynFit Cutting Edge, or LynFit Power Shot.

Excess caffeine has been shown to cause insomnia, headaches, dizziness, rapid or abnormal heart rhythm, dehydration, and anxiety.

When it comes to caffeine, every person is different. Sixty milligrams is a good starting point, and everyone should limit caffeine to 60mg or less per hour to avoid overdosing, which can backfire when it comes to weight loss and fat burning. Remember the LynFit motto: Go big because now you can! You can always add more if needed.

NOT SURE HOW TO MAKE GREAT-TASTING COFFEE?

Making great tasting coffee doesn't require much. All you need is some good beans, a French press and about five minutes. Forget the store-bought artificial stuff or ready to drink coffees. They hide tons of sugar and artificial flavors in them, especially bottled versions. The best is to GO BLACK, keep it clean and lean.

WHEN IT COMES TO FLAVOR, GO BOLD!

There's nothing worse than a weak cup of coffee. The secret is knowing the correct water-to-coffee ratio without wasting coffee through multiple rounds of trial and error.

According to the National Coffee Association, the correct ration is one to two tablespoons of ground coffee for every six ounces of water. So, the next time you begin brewing, start out with this guideline, and then adjust according to your taste preferences.

The Europeans know how to do this best. They brew small batches (1-2 cups) because they know coffee gets more acidic and tastes bitter after sitting. This is not in your head, leaving coffee exposed to air can cause flavors and aromas to go stale. Coffee grounds are full of oils, acids, and molecules that oxidize and make coffee taste sour the longer they are in contact with air.

Not only that, the more you expose the beans to hot water (like reheating our mug), and the more oxidation occurs. Aim to finish your cup of joe within 20 minutes, and brew small batches at-a-time versus large ones.

DON'T QUIT WHAT YOU LOVE

Most people quit drinking coffee when trying to lose weight, which is sad because coffee has many health benefits and helps keep our body naturally energized, and our brains focused.

Why do most people give up on such a healthy drink? They haven't learned how to enjoy it black, or they simply don't like the taste of black coffee. For most, it's about cream and sugar, and I totally get that. No judgement here! I was the same way until I learned how to combine my morning Metabolic Boosting Protein Shake in it. Now, instead of the occasional cappuccino treat, I have one every day.

Why should you give up your morning cup of coffee made with milk and whatever else you're adding, even if it is *just a little*? This includes soy, almond, and coconut milk. Because what you're adding to it IS NOT going to help you lose weight, and it blocks the burning off dangerous belly fat. It's just that simple.

WHY IS DAIRY SO BAD FOR WEIGHT LOSS?

Dairy can be high in calories, saturated fat, and cholesterol — substances that have been associated with increased blood sugar levels. This makes it easy to gain weight and more difficult to lose it.

Elevated blood sugar levels block fat burning, especially belly fat, that is more harmful than you realize when it comes to your health and losing weight.

If you're wondering how LynFit's whey can be okay for even the most dairy sensitive, it's because we specialize in difficult metabolisms, and we know firsthand how bad milk and its replacements are when it comes to trying to lose weight. I personally cannot do dairy, so we take things a step further and make sure our whey is micro-filtered to remove all traces of lactose, so all that's left is the super-nutritious benefits. You get all the benefits and none of the guilt or harmful side effects that lactose causes most people as they age, or if trying to lose weight.

Now your coffee isn't only the best part of waking up, it's also the best possible thing you can do for whole-body health, and making it faster and easier to lose weight, while killing cravings and keeping you feeling full for up to six hours.

Without further delay, I'll kick the Metabolic Clean Cafe section off with my superstar non-dairy, lactose-free Metabolic Melt Fat Milk. It's the only milk that's good for your metabolism and boosts health every time you drink it!

You can shake with it, bake with it, pour it over your fruit, add it to your coffee or tea, or even use it with your cereal or oatmeal. It's pure protein, lactose-free, chock full of essential amino acids, and five grams of prebiotic fiber that balances blood sugar levels and improves whole-body health, including gut health.

You can decide between Vanilla Creme, Chocolate Truffle, Wild Strawberry, or Salted Caramel. Make sure you always have some prepared to use in a pinch!

If your waist is as big as your hips, you'll want to make these delicious changes as soon as possible. Be ritualistic about them to keep your health and weight in check.

METABOLIC MELT FAT MILK
(METABOLIC MILK REPLACER)

Ingredients:

- (2 scoops) LynFit Vanilla Protein Powder, or protein powder flavor of choice
- (½ cup) Water
- Handful of ice

Put all the ingredients into a blender or shaker cup and mix well.

CLEANER CAPPUCCINO WITH FAT BURNING FROTH

The secret to frothing your protein shake lies in the purity and freshness of LynFit's proteins. They are microfiltered, lactose-free, and do not contain any fillers, preservatives, or inferior ingredients that weigh protein down, preventing it from frothing up. Everyone loves a good froth, especially on top of their coffee. It makes the perfect **Cleaner Cappuccino**!

- Add cold water to a clean, good quality blender
- Add (½ cup) of LynFit Protein Powder
- Blend on medium speed for 1-2 minutes, or until it froths to the desired amount
- Spoon onto hot black coffee and sprinkle with some LynFit Sinful Chocolate Sauce or LynFit Chocolate Whey Protein

If your froth flops, add some ice. If your shake doesn't froth, it may be due to your water or blender. Use bottled water without the minerals.

FAT MELTING MOCHACCINO

- In a blender, mix (½ cup) of cold water (you can add more or less water depending on the consistency you prefer).
- Add (2 scoops) LynFit Chocolate Truffle Protein Powder.
- Add (1 tsp.) of granulated instant coffee.
- Gradually add (5) ice cubes to thicken.

Blend on high for one minute (in a pinch, this shake can also be made by simply mixing ingredients together in a glass with a spoon). Drink yourself skinny!

ICED CHAI LATTE

Ingredients:

- (2 scoops) French Vanilla Crème or Chocolate Truffle Protein Powder
- (½ cup) Chai tea
- (5) ice cubes

Put all the ingredients into a blender or shaker cup and mix well.

EXTREME SALTED CARAMEL TOFFEE LATTE

Freeze your glass ahead of time and prepare your Sinful Chocolate Sauce that's loaded with good-for-your-gut prebiotic fiber (10 grams) to drizzle inside.

Preparation:

- (1 tbsp.) Cold water (or less for a thicker sauce) mixed with (1 tbsp.) LynFit Sinful Chocolate Sauce
- Place in the refrigerator to thicken

Ingredients:

- (2 scoops) Lynfit Salted Carmel Protein Powder
- (½ cup) Water (or desired amount)
- (1 tsp.) Granulated coffee
- (4-5) Ice cubes

Blend protein powder to desired consistency. Drizzle in the chocolate or paint with a spoon for the desired look and enjoy!

FAT BURNING FLAT WHITE

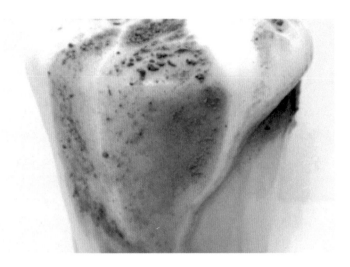

The Flat White is the Australian answer to the latte. If you're in need of a protein boost and a lover of the steamed froth, you'll love the Flat White. I love the froth so much I eat mine with a spoon like dessert!

Ingredients:

- (2 scoops) LynFit French Vanilla Crème Protein Powder
- (½–1 cup) Pre-made black coffee or espresso

Blend or shake in a shaker cup until frothy (better blended). Microwave for 30 seconds or less to heat it up a bit.

METABOLIC BOOSTING HOT CHOCOLATE

You can substitute LynFit French Vanilla Crème Protein Powder for a White Chocolate and LynFit Salted Caramel Protein Powder for a Salted Caramel Chocolate.

Ingredients:

- (2 scoops) LynFit Chocolate Truffle Protein Powder
- (½–1 cup) Warm water

Put all the ingredients into a blender or shaker cup and mix well or microwave for 30 seconds to warm (be careful not to overheat).

Can be easily made into an Iced Hot Chocolate by simply adding ice.

HOMEMADE CINNAMON DOLCE STEAMER

Wanna make your morning a little sweeter without all the calories, fat, or excess sugar? This delicious, metabolic boosting cinnamon dolce steamer will knock your socks off! It's as delicious as it is nutritious and even helps lower blood sugar levels, which helps kill hunger and cravings.

This easy recipe is an exact replica of Starbucks' sweet, warm, and comforting Cinnamon Dolce Latte, but cleaner. It's perfect for the holidays and chilly weather sipping or anytime you want something delicious, without wrecking your diet.

The LynFit Complete Protein Powder is sweet and creamy, so there is no need to add brown sugar to this recipe unless you want it even sweeter. I suggest Equal® brown sugar versus regular brown sugar to avoid insulin spikes that block fat burning.

Take out the cinnamon, and you've got a Vanilla Steamer!

Ingredients:

- (6 oz.) Warm water
- (1-2 tsp.) Instant espresso powder
- (2 scoops) French Vanilla Crème Complete Protein Powder
- (½ cup) Pre-made Melt Fat Milk (see the previous Melt Fat Milk recipe)
- (¼ tsp.) Ground cinnamon
- (½ tsp.) Pure vanilla extract *Optional
- (Pinch) Ground nutmeg
- Ground cinnamon for garnish

Directions:

- Stir the espresso powder into the warm water and set aside.
- Prepare the Melt Fat Milk in a glass measuring cup by combining the protein powder, cinnamon, and nutmeg; stir until thoroughly combined.
- Place in microwave and cook for 30-45 seconds, or until Melt Fat Milk starts to froth up. *DO NOT overcook or it will curdle.
- Remove from Microwave and stir again if needed.
- Place in Microwave for an additional 30 seconds, or until the milk starts to froth up again.
- Remove and, while stirring the espresso, slowly pour the milk mixture into the coffee.
- Garnish with cinnamon.
- INDULGE!

PEPPERMINT HOT CHOCOLATE

Ingredients:

- (2 scoops) LynFit Chocolate Truffle Protein
- (1 cup) Warm water
- Peppermint tea bag

Note: This recipe can also be made without a blender.

Simply stir until dissolved. Vanilla Protein may also be used rather than Chocolate.

Heat water until warm (not boiling) to brew the tea. Add the Chocolate Protein to brewed peppermint tea and stir until blended. It can be made in a blender as well if desired.

It can be made into a latte as well.

CHOCOLATE LOVERS METABOLIC BOOSTING SMOOTHIES

Yes, indeed, this section is all about the super-delicious and nutritious superfood cacao and the bliss it delivers. Chocolate lovers, this section is for you. And yes, you can and should have this chocolate for breakfast!

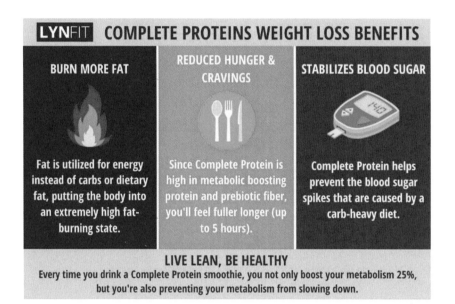

LYNFIT **COMPLETE PROTEINS WEIGHT LOSS BENEFITS**

BURN MORE FAT	REDUCED HUNGER & CRAVINGS	STABILIZES BLOOD SUGAR
Fat is utilized for energy instead of carbs or dietary fat, putting the body into an extremely high fat-burning state.	Since Complete Protein is high in metabolic boosting protein and prebiotic fiber, you'll feel fuller longer (up to 5 hours).	Complete Protein helps prevent the blood sugar spikes that are caused by a carb-heavy diet.

LIVE LEAN, BE HEALTHY

Every time you drink a Complete Protein smoothie, you not only boost your metabolism 25%, but you're also preventing your metabolism from slowing down.

CHOCOLATE JAVA BOOST

Ingredients:

- (2 scoops) LynFit Chocolate Truffle Protein Powder
- (½ cup) Water or black coffee
- (1 tbsp.) Instant coffee
- Handful of ice

Blend the above ingredients until desired consistency is reached.

CHOCOLATE PEANUT BUTTER CUP

Ingredients:

- (2 scoops) LynFit Chocolate Truffle Protein Powder
- (½ cup) Water
- (½ tbsp.) Powdered peanut butter
- Handful of ice

Put all the ingredients into a blender or shaker cup and mix well.

CHOCOLATE BLISS BOMB

Ingredients:

- (2 scoops) LynFit Chocolate Truffle Protein Powder
- (1-2 tbsp.) LynFit Sinful Chocolate Sauce
- (1 cup) Water (for a thicker shake, use less water – creamier, lighter, use more water)
- (5+) Large ice cubes

Make a little extra chocolate sauce to drizzle inside the glass.

Combine ingredients in a blender until desired consistency is reached.

WHITE CHOCOLATE TRUFFLE

Ingredients:

- (1 scoop) LynFit Chocolate Truffle Complete Protein
- (1 scoop) LynFit French Vanilla Crème Complete Protein
- (¾ cup) Water
- Handful of ice (optional)

Combine ingredients in a blender until desired consistency is reached.

PEPPERMINT PATTY THAT POWERS METABOLISM

Ingredients:

- (2 scoops) LynFit Chocolate Truffle Protein Powder
- (¾ cup) Pre-made mint tea
- Handful of ice (optional)

*For a bolder flavor, brew tea longer or add a few sprigs of mint leaves.

Put all the ingredients into a blender or shaker cup and mix well.

CHOCOLATE ALMOND BREEZE

Ingredients:

- (2 scoops) LynFit Chocolate Truffle Protein Powder
- (1 tsp.) Zero-calorie almond-flavored syrup
- (¾ cup) Water
- Handful of ice (optional)

Put all the ingredients into a blender or shaker cup and mix well.

CHOCOLATE SALTED CARAMEL TOFFEE DREAM

Ingredients:

- (1 scoop) LynFit Chocolate Truffle Protein Powder
- (1 scoop) LynFit Salted Caramel Protein Powder
- (¾ cup) Water
- Handful of ice (optional)

Put all the ingredients into a blender or shaker cup and mix well.

CHOCOLATE COVERED STRAWBERRY LOVE

Ingredients:

- (1 scoop) LynFit Chocolate Truffle Protein Powder
- (1 scoop) LynFit Wild Strawberry Protein Powder
- (¾ cup) Water
- Handful of ice (optional)

Put all the ingredients into a blender and mix well.

For a thicker style pudding-like smoothie, reduce the water and add more ice.

FROZEN HOT CHOCOLATE

Ingredients:

- (2 scoops) LynFit Chocolate Truffle Protein Powder
- (1 tbsp.) LynFit Sinful Chocolate Sauce
- (½ cup) Very cold water
- Handful of ice

Put all the ingredients into a blender or shaker cup and mix well. Serve in a large mug (pre-freeze first for a real treat).

For additional yumminess, you'll want to make extra Sinful Chocolate Sauce to drizzle inside the glass!

THE CLASSIC CHOCOLATE MILKSHAKE

Ingredients:

- (2 scoops) LynFit Chocolate Truffle Protein Powder
- (¾ cup) Water
- Handful of ice (optional)

Combine ingredients and blend until desired consistency is reached.

For an extra treat, drizzle some Sinful Chocolate Sauce to drizzle inside the glass!

GOOD FOR YOUR METABOLISM GREEN DRINK

While greens (the chlorophyll) may not be as delicious as chocolate, greens deserve some love too. Smoothies are a perfect way to get your greens in if you're one of those *"I hate veggies"* people.

What makes this smoothie different than any other smoothie recipe you'll find is that it is good for your metabolism and won't cause blood sugar spikes or thyroid function, and it's reduced-fat because we use less, or omit, the worst offending goitrogenic vegetables.

The Go Green, Be Lean Smoothie has everything your body needs to nourish your hair, skin, and nails while preserving lean muscle with lean protein, and replenishing your electrolytes, vitamins, and minerals. All in one delicious smoothie. It doesn't get better than this!

HATE VEGETABLES?

That's okay. Our LynFit Sinful Chocolate Sauce is just as healthy. Add (1 tsp.) to your Green Smoothie!

- Low-fat, zero sugar, 10 grams of prebiotic fiber
- Improves circulation, Improves cognitive performance
- Increases stamina

Sinful Chocolate Sauce has more antioxidants than most superfoods. Its ORAC score is 95,500, beating out the famous Goji Berry (well-known as one of the most nutritionally packed superfoods in the world to anyone interested in living a healthy lifestyle), which has an ORAC score of just 25,300.

We all know how awesome blueberries, spinach, and kale are for helping stomp out free radicals, due to their abundance of antioxidants; however, none of them can even come close to LynFit's Sinful Chocolate Sauce!

GOOD FOR YOUR METABOLISM GREEN DRINK

Ingredients:

- (2 scoops) LynFit French Vanilla Crème Protein Powder
- (1 cup) Cold water (filtered is best, use more if desired)
- Handful of ice cubes
- Handful of Romaine lettuce
- Small handful of parsley
- (½) Cucumber
- (1 oz. or 1 shot) LynFit Daily Power Shot
- (1 dropper-full) LynFit Vitamin D3 Boost

Combine ingredients in a blender until desired consistency is reached.

Want more health and healing? You can add (1small piece) of ginger, (½ cup) of pineapple, or juice from a lime. More stress relief? Add LynFit Thryo-Boost or LynFit CBD Daily Wellness.

METABOLIC SUPER-FRUITS & VEGGIES

Fresh or frozen fruit make these metabolic boosting smoothies even more delicious and nutritious. These recipes were specifically chosen due to their low glycemic (blood sugar) response that's also blunted by the prebiotic fiber in LynFit's Complete Protein Powder.

Now you can enjoy a little fruit without wrecking your waistline!

HOW CAN YOU ADD FRUIT (SUCH AS A GREEN APPLE) AND NOT WRECK YOUR WAISTLINE?

Because you're mixing the fruit with LynFit's Complete Protein that's high in metabolic boosting, blood sugar lowering protein, and prebiotic fiber, that bounces blood sugar spikes!

Adding a serving of Complete Protein Powder adds 24 grams of protein to your smoothie and makes it a more filling, better-balanced meal that helps balance blood sugars levels. But not all protein powders are created equal. LynFit's is the best when it comes to helping you manage your blood sugar levels, making it easier to lose weight and melt fat.

RASPBERRY KETONE FAT BURNING ACCELERATOR

Ingredients:

- (2 scoops) LynFit Protein Powder – any flavor
- (¾ cup) Water
- (½ cup) Raspberries – fresh or frozen
- Handful of ice (optional)

Combine ingredients in a blender until desired consistency is reached.

Want more energy and a craving killer? Open a capsule of LynFit Accelerator Advanced with Raspberry Ketones (aka Keto Carb Edge) and pour it into your smoothie.

BLUEBERRY HEALTH BOOST

Ingredients:

- (2 scoops) LynFit French Vanilla Crème Protein Powder
- (½ cup) Blueberries – fresh or frozen
- (¾ cup) Water
- Handful of ice (optional)

Did you know that adding Complete Protein Powder can blunt blood sugar spikes that can come from consuming fruit?

Combine ingredients in a blender until desired consistency is reached.

WILD STRAWBERRY BLISS

Ingredients:

- (2 scoops) LynFit French Vanilla Crème Protein Powder
- (½ - 1 cup) Strawberries – fresh or frozen
- (¾ cup) Water
- Handful of ice (optional)

Combine ingredients in a blender until desired consistency is reached.

Make it lemonade by adding a stick packet of Crystal Light® lemonade.

BANANA CREAM TO BE LEAN

Ingredients:

- (2 scoops) LynFit French Vanilla Crème Protein Powder
- (½) Banana – frozen (fresh works too, but frozen is better)
- (¾ cup) Water
- Handful of ice (optional)

Combine ingredients in a blender until desired consistency is reached.

STRAWBERRY BANANA BOOSTER

Ingredients:

- (2 scoops) LynFit Wild Strawberry Protein Powder
- (½) Banana – frozen (fresh works too, but frozen is better)
- (¾ cup) Water
- Handful of ice (optional)

Combine ingredients in a blender until desired consistency is reached.

ENZYME HEALING PINA COLADA

Ingredients:

- (1 scoop) LynFit French Vanilla Creme Protein Powder
- (1 scoop) LynFit Wild Strawberry Protein Powder
- (½) Pineapple
- (1 oz./1 shot) LynFit Daily Joint Repair
- (¾ cup) Water
- Handful of ice (optional)

Combine ingredients in a blender until desired consistency is reached.

This enzyme-healing smoothies helps strengthen your immune system and works in conjunction with nutrients to repair cells and build health, so you eat less

CHERRY GARCIA

Ingredients:

- (2 scoops) LynFit French Vanilla Creme Protein Powder
- (½-¾ cup) Cherries – frozen (fresh works too, but frozen is better)
- (¾ cup) Water
- Handful of ice (optional)

Combine ingredients in a blender until desired consistency is reached.

- Helps alleviate insomnia
- Lowers hypertension
- Maintains our body's proper pH balance

CREAMY CARROT CAKE

Ingredients:

- (2½ - 3 scoops) LynFit French Vanilla Creme Protein Powder, or whichever LynFit Protein you prefer (using more shake makes it thick and creamy, like the real thing)
- (½ - 1 cup) Cold water (less water creates a thicker shake)
- (½ cup) Cooked carrots (I use frozen pre-thawed)
- (¼ tsp.) Cinnamon
- (1/8 tsp.) Nutmeg
- Ice, if needed

Combine ingredients in a blender until desired consistency is reached.

SUMMERTIME WATERMELON FOR WEIGHT LOSS

Ingredients:

- (2 scoops) LynFit French Vanilla Creme Protein Powder (delicious with Wild Strawberry too)
- (1 cup) Watermelon - diced
- Handful of ice (optional)

Combine ingredients in a blender until desired consistency is reached.

For an extra special boost, add a few sprigs of mint Leaves and (1 tsp.) of lime juice.

APPLE PIE IN A GLASS

Ingredients:

- (2 scoops) LynFit Salted Caramel Protein Powder
- (½ cup) Water
- (1 small) Apple - chopped into smaller pieces for easier blending (Tart green is delicious and contains less sugar)
- (5) Ice cubes

Combine ingredients in a blender until desired consistency is reached.

Customers call this the "filler-upper" because it keeps you feeling full for up to five hours.

HEALTH & HEALING BOOSTERS

These metabolic boosting smoothies are specifically designed to make you look, feel, and BE better while promoting weight loss and accelerating fat burning. You'll not just be leaner, but you'll also be healthier and stronger too!

THE NATURAL ENERGIZER
(AKA Booze-Free)

The Natural Energizer Protein Shake (also known as the Morning After drink) provides energy that nourishes with over 90 essential vitamins, minerals, enzymes. Feeling better begins with nourishing your body. You would have to juice over 30 pounds of vegetables to match the nutrition found in this shake!

Ingredients:

- (2 scoops) LynFit French Vanilla Crème Protein Powder
- (½ cup) Water
- (1 oz./1 shot) LynFit Daily Power Shot
- Handful of ice

Combine ingredients in a blender until desired consistency is reached.

THE BEAUTY SMOOTHIE
(AKA Skin-Tightening)

Ingredients:

- (2 scoops) LynFit French Vanilla Crème Protein Powder
- (1 cup) Cold water – filtered preferred
- (1 oz./1 shot) LynFit Daily Power Shot
- (1 oz./1 shot) LynFit Daily Joint Repair or Thyro-Boost
- (½ cup) Raspberries (or any berry)
- Handful of ice

Combine ingredients in a blender until desired consistency is reached.

BERRY BRAIN BOOST

Ingredients:

- (2 scoops) LynFit French Vanilla Crème Protein Powder
- (½-¾ cup) Cold water – filtered preferred
- (½ cup) Blueberries (fresh or frozen)
- (1 oz./1 shot) LynFit Daily Power Shot
- Handful of ice

Combine ingredients in a blender until desired consistency is reached.

Don't forget your LynFit Pure Omega 3 to balance out nutrition.

CLEANSING DETOXIFIER (To Kickstart Weight Loss)

This cleansing detoxifier is the only one of its kind because it boosts metabolism and is loaded with alkalinizing greens that won't block thyroid function or spike insulin levels the way most juices and green smoothies can.

Ingredients:

- (2 scoops) LynFit French Vanilla Crème Protein Powder
- (¾ cup) Cold water – filtered/spring water preferred
- (½) Cucumber, peeled and diced
- Handful of spinach or Romaine lettuce
- Squeeze (½) lemon for juice
- (½ dropper-full) LynFit Thyro-Boost
- Handful of ice

Combine ingredients in a blender until desired consistency is reached.

PEACHES-N-CREAM (Joint Healing Optimizer)

Nourishing your body should also include your joints, tendons, and ligaments to help balance inflammation, relieve pain, and protect them from deteriorating to keep them flexible and make movement easier. Adding Daily Joint Repair is the fastest and most effective way to do just that.

Ingredients:

- (2 scoops) LynFit French Vanilla Crème Protein Powder
- (¾ cup) Cold water – filtered preferred
- (½ cup) Peaches (fresh or frozen)
- (1 oz./1 shot) LynFit Daily Joint Repair
- (5) Ice cubes

Combine ingredients in a blender until desired consistency is reached.

HYDRATING LEMON BERRY WITH ELECTROLYTES

Ingredients:

- (2 scoops) LynFit French Vanilla Crème Protein Powder
- (1 cup) Spring water or filtered water
- (1 oz./1 shot) LynFit Daily Power Shot
- (½-1) Lemon, juiced (according to taste)
- (½ cup) Frozen blueberries
- Handful of ice

Combine ingredients in a blender until desired consistency is reached.

FAT BLASTING CINNAMON ROLL

Cinnamon, combined with prebiotic fiber, is one of the best ways to control blood sugar levels and flip the fat-burning switch to on and the weight gain switch to off.

Ingredients:

- (2 scoops) LynFit French Vanilla Crème Protein Powder
- (½ cup) Water
- (1 tsp.) Cinnamon
- Handful of ice

Combine ingredients in a blender until desired consistency is reached.

HORMONE BALANCER

The #1 rule when it comes to losing weight, whether you're male or female (especially if you have a stubborn metabolism or carry excess belly fat), is balance your hormones, and then you can lose weight. One of these every day can be just what your body needs.

Ingredients:

- (2 scoops) LynFit Wild Strawberry Protein Powder
- (1 cup) Cold water – filtered preferred
- (½ cup) Raspberries (or any berry)
- (1-2 dropper-fulls) LynFit Thyro-Boost
- Handful of ice

Combine ingredients in a blender until desired consistency is reached.

THYROID HEALTH BOOSTER

Ingredients:

- (2 scoops) LynFit Wild Strawberry Protein Powder
- (1 cup) Water – filtered preferred
- (1 dropper-full) LynFit Thyro-Boost
- (½ cup) Pineapple
- Handful of ice

Combine ingredients in a blender until desired consistency is reached.

BONE STRENGTHENER, BLOOD BUILDER

Strong bones are made in the kitchen and, when combined with weight training, can reverse osteoporosis and help you avoid expensive medications with a long list of side effects.

Ingredients:

- (2 scoops) LynFit French Vanilla Crème Protein Powder
- (1 cup) Water – filtered preferred
- (1 oz./1 shot) LynFit Daily Power Shot
- (1 oz./1 shot) LynFit Daily Joint Repair
- (½ cup) Pineapple (optional for enzymes)
- Handful of ice

Combine ingredients in a blender until desired consistency is reached.

MEGA IMMUNE BOOST PINK DRINK

Ingredients:

- (2 scoops) LynFit Wild Strawberry Protein Powder
- (1 cup) Pre-made green tea
- (1 oz./1 shot) LynFit Daily Power Shot
- (1 dropper-full) LynFit Vitamin D3 Boost
- (1 dropper-full) LynFit Daily Wellness CBD Liquid Drops
- (½ cup) Raspberries or cherries
- Handful of ice

Combine ingredients in a blender until desired consistency is reached. The next time you aren't feeling well, think LynFit Pink Drink!

AWARD WINNING K.I.S.S. ANTI-INFLAMMATORY

This smoothie has won awards when it comes to best-tasting and reducing inflammation; not only because of what it has in it, but also for what it doesn't.

Most smoothies are made using too much sugar, saturated fats, or ingredients that are said to be allergens, which increases inflammation. Not this smoothie. It's our K.I.S.S. smoothie! We keep it simple for the best results.

You don't need to add teeth-staining, non-absorbing turmeric, or nasty tasting ingredients because LynFit has you covered. Supplementing with these healing nutrients is superior to trying to ingest them through your smoothies because you can get the specific amount required for the best results. This way, your smoothie stays delicious and nutritious.

Ingredients:

- (2 scoops) LynFit Protein Powder – flavor of choice
- (1 cup) Pre-made green or black tea
- (1 oz./1 shot) LynFit Daily Power Shot
- (1 oz./1 shot) LynFit Daily Joint Repair
- (1 dropper-full) Vitamin D3 Boost
- (½ cup) Papaya and/or pineapple
- (1 tbsp.) Flax seeds or flaxseed oil (optional) – you can substitute LynFit Pure Omega 3 if you don't have flaxseed
- Handful of ice

Combine ingredients in a blender until desired consistency is reached.

HEALTHY HOLIDAY SMOOTHIES

Saved the best for last! Chocolate isn't the only dessert food we've metabolized, healthified, and forced into a blender. You won't want to miss these delicious and nutritious eats.

Wanna turn your protein shake into ice cream?

Freeze it until the desired consistency is reached and enjoy! Or, for instant ice cream, combine (2 scoops) of LynFit Complete Protein Powder with a (½ cup) of frozen fruit in a blender or food processor and blend until it's ice cream. It's that simple.

Or, freeze it in a Dixie cup, popsicle mold, or turn it into a smoothie bowl by using less water and adding more ice. **The only limit is your imagination!**

PEANUT BUTTER & JELLY BOOST

Ingredients:

- (1 scoop) LynFit Wild Strawberry Protein Powder
- (1 scoop) LynFit French Vanilla Crème Protein Powder
- (1 cup) Cold water
- (1 tsp.) PB2 powder or peanut butter
- (¼ cup) Blueberries
- (¼ cup) Strawberries
- Handful of ice (optional)

Combine ingredients in a blender until desired consistency is reached.

BANANA SPLIT

Ingredients:

- (2 scoops) LynFit Chocolate Truffle Protein Powder
- (1 cup) Cold water
- (1) Frozen banana
- Handful of ice (optional)

Combine ingredients in a blender until desired consistency is reached.

Want more flavor? Add (1 tsp.) of sugar-free banana pudding. Garnish with LynFit Sinful Chocolate Sauce made as syrup to drizzle inside or rim the glass.

CHOCOLATE OATMEAL COOKIE FOR BREAKFAST

Ingredients:

- (2 scoops) LynFit Chocolate Truffle Protein Powder
- (1 cup) Cold water
- (½) Small banana
- (½ cup) Oatmeal
- (1 tbsp.) Raw almond, cashew, or peanut butter
- Handful of ice (optional)

Combine ingredients in a blender until desired consistency is reached.

Garnish with mini-chocolate chips.

This recipe is great for maintenance or anyone who may need additional calories.

RASPBERRY CHEESECAKE

Ingredients:

- (2 scoops) LynFit Wild Strawberry Protein Powder
- (1 cup) Cold water
- (1 cup) Frozen raspberries
- (1 tsp. – 1 tbsp.) Sugar-free cheesecake pudding mix
- (1 tbsp.) Raw almond, cashew, or peanut butter
- Handful of ice (optional)

Combine ingredients in a blender until desired consistency is reached.

Garnish with raspberries or sprinkle a little graham cracker on top.

This recipe is great for maintenance or anyone who may need additional calories. To lower calories, swap out nut butter for PB2 powder.

APPLE SALTED CARAMEL COBBLER

Ingredients:

- (2 scoops) LynFit Salted Caramel Protein Powder
- (1 cup) Cold water
- (1 cup) Diced or sliced apple – green is better
- Dash of cinnamon and/or nutmeg
- Handful of ice (optional)

Topping to make it magical: (1 tbsp.) of oats mixed with a little LynFit French Vanilla Crème Protein Powder (and/or Splenda® brown sugar) and a tiny bit of Smart Balance® and dash of cinnamon.

Combine ingredients in a blender until desired consistency is reached.

You can also layer the apples instead of combining them for a layered texture.

PUMPKIN PIE POWER BOOST

Ingredients:

- (2 scoops) LynFit Salted Caramel Protein Powder
- (1 cup) Cold water
- Dash of cinnamon, nutmeg, or pumpkin spice
- Handful of ice (optional)

Topping to make it magical: (1 tbsp.) of oats mixed with a little LynFit French Vanilla Crème Protein Powder (and/or Splenda® brown sugar) and a tiny bit of Smart Balance® and dash of cinnamon.

Combine ingredients in a blender until desired consistency is reached.

EGG NOG NOT

Ingredients:

- (2 scoops) LynFit French Vanilla Crème or Chocolate Truffle Protein Powder
- (1 cup) Cold water or calorie-free coconut water
- (½) Frozen banana
- (½ tsp.) Ground nutmeg
- (½ tsp.) Ground cinnamon
- Dash of cardamom
- Handful of ice (optional)

Topping to make it magical: (1 tbsp.) of shredded coconut.

Combine ingredients in a blender until desired consistency is reached.

BE LEAN BUTTERFINGER

What could be better than a Butterfinger? One taste and you'll know why they say, "Always keep one at your desk!" Here is the better way to enjoy Butterfinger.

Ingredients:

- (2 scoops) LynFit Salted Caramel Protein Powder
- (1 cup) Cold water or calorie-free coconut water
- (½) Frozen banana
- (1 tbsp.) Sugar-free butterscotch pudding mix
- (1-2 tbsp.) PB2 powder (optional)
- Handful of ice (optional)

Topping to make it magical: (1 tbsp.) of shredded coconut.

Combine ingredients in a blender until desired consistency is reached.

CHOCOLATE MOUNDS FOR YOUR METABOLISM

This is my #2, or if I'm being honest ... tied for #1, dessert shake. I'm in full agreement with Hershey's when they say that, "Every coconut has a dream to one day find itself covered in chocolate and almonds. "Pure decadence coconut with rich dark chocolate, without all of the added calories!

Ingredients:

- (2 scoops) LynFit Chocolate Truffle Protein Powder
- (1 cup) Cold water or calorie-free coconut water
- (1 tsp.) Coconut extract
- (1 tsp.) Almond extract
- Handful of ice (optional)

Combine ingredients in a blender until desired consistency is reached.

Optional: Drizzle LynFit Sinful Chocolate Sauce on the inside of the glass.

79

KETO SKINNY SNICKERS

Snickers'® slogan is "Making hungry people into happy people." It's my personal favorite, so finding a healthier way to enjoy it was a top priority for me, and it's been a phenomenal success!

Ingredients:

- (1 scoop) LynFit Chocolate Truffle Protein Powder
- (1 scoop) LynFit Salted Caramel Protein Powder
- (1 cup) Cold water
- (1 tbsp.) PB2 or regular, unsweetened peanut butter
- (1 tsp.) Zero-calorie almond-flavored syrup
- Handful of ice (optional)

Combine ingredients in a blender until desired consistency is reached.

Optional: Drizzle LynFit Sinful Chocolate Sauce on the inside of the glass.

BE LEAN BIRTHDAY CAKE (KETO-FRIENDLY)

The Be Lean Birthday Cake Protein Shake will help you burn calories versus storing them. Low-calorie, low-carb, no sugar... Oh my!

Ingredients:

- (3 scoops) LynFit French Vanilla Crème Protein Powder
- (1 cup) Cold water
- Handful of ice

Combine ingredients in a blender until desired consistency is reached.

Optional: Garnish with sprinkles or drizzle LynFit Sinful Chocolate Sauce on the inside of the glass.

LEMONCELLO FOR YOUR METABOLISM

Ingredients:

- (2 scoops) LynFit French Vanilla Crème Protein Powder
- (¾ cup) Cold water
- (1 stick packet) Crystal Light® lemonade (for a milder flavor, use the juice of a lemon)
- Handful of ice cubes

Combine ingredients in a blender until desired consistency is reached.

SUPER KETO TWIZZLER

Ingredients:

- (2 scoops) LynFit Wild Strawberry Protein Powder
- (1 cup) Cold water
- (1 cup) Frozen strawberries
- (1 tsp. – 1 tbsp.) Sugar-free strawberry pudding mix
- Handful of ice (optional)

Combine ingredients in a blender until desired consistency is reached.

Garnish with a Twizzler® stick!

CREAMY KETO DREAMSICLE

Ingredients:

- (2 scoops) LynFit French Vanilla Crème Protein Powder
- (1 cup) Cold water
- (1) Orange, peeled
- (½) Frozen banana
- Handful of ice (optional)

Combine ingredients in a blender until desired consistency is reached.

Got high blood sugar? Use sugar-free orange Jello® instead

METABOLIC SUPPORT PRODUCT OVERVIEW

Find your perfect health and metabolic boosting combination of healing powers, natural energizers, Immune boosting, or strength building nutrients.

For more detailed information and a complete list of all we have to offer, please visit LynFit.com.

METABOLIC BOOSTING COMPLETE PROTEIN
With prebiotic fiber in four delicious flavors

DAILY POWER SHOT
With Resveratrol, liquid antioxidants, vitamins, minerals, and enzymes

DAILY JOINT REPAIR
With hyaluronic acid, fast-acting liquid pain relief and repair

ADAPTOGENIC THYRO-BOOST
With ashwagandha, liquid plant-based detoxifying, cleansing, hormonal-balancing

VITAMIN D3 BOOST
Unparalleled fusion of vitamin D mixed with beta-glucans in the most bioavailable form for maximum immunity support

DAILY WELLNESS CBD LIQUID DROPS (also available as gummies)
Plant-based, THC-free cannabinoids and Phyto-compounds in the purest, fullest strength available

SINFUL CHOCOLATE SAUCE
With prebiotic fiber that is a delicious and nutritious superfood that's good for your metabolism

LEAN BARS
With prebiotic fiber, it's the only protein bar available that promotes weight loss and accelerates fat-burning

CONCLUSION

I hope you enjoy these delicious, nutritous smoothies that are good for your metabolism and improve every aspect of your health. My mission was to create something that tastes so good that you begin to crave it.

You can't change what you don't know, and NOW you know that NOT all smoothies are good for weight loss or your health.

Here's to your health, and God bless you!
Lisa and the LynFit Team

71703491R00059